ideals
EASTER
2005

Dedicated to a celebration of the American ideals of faith in God, loyalty to country, and love of family.

Features

Departments

Cover: Exuberant pink tulips and delicate white azaleas welcome visitors to the Sherwood Gardens in Baltimore, Maryland. Photograph by William H. Johnson.

Inside front cover: Delicate tulips and golden pears are the focal point of this still-life painting, WINTER BLOOMS, by Mary Kay Krell. Copyright © Mary Kay Krell. All rights reserved.

IDEALS—Vol. 62, No. 1 January 2005 IDEALS (ISSN 0019-137X, USPS 256-240) is published six times a year: January, March, May, July, September, and November by IDEALS PUBLICATIONS, a division of Guideposts, 39 Seminary Hill Road, Carmel, NY 10512. Copyright © 2005 by IDEALS PUBLICATIONS, a division of Guideposts. All rights reserved. The cover and entire contents of IDEALS are fully protected by copyright and must not be reproduced in any manner whatsoever. Title IDEALS registered U.S. Patent Office. Printed and bound in USA. Printed on Weyerhaeuser Husky. The paper used in this publication meets the minimum requirements of American National Standard for Information Sciences—Permanence of Paper for Printed Library Materials, ANSI Z39.48-1984. Periodicals postage paid at Carmel, New York, and additional mailing offices. Canadian mailed under Publications Mail Agreement Number 40010140. POST-MASTER: Send address changes to IDEALS, 39 Seminary Hill Road, Carmel, NY 10512. CANADA POST: Send address changes to Guideposts PO Box 1051, Fort Erie ON L2A 6C7. For subscription or customer service questions, contact IDEALS Publications, a division of Guideposts, 39 Seminary Hill Road, Carmel, NY 10512. Fax 845-228-2115. Reader Preference Service: We occasionally make our mailing lists available to other companies whose products or services might interest you. If you prefer not to be included, please write to Ideals Customer Service.

ISBN 0-8249-1300-0 GST 893989236

Visit the *Ideals* website
at www.idealsbooks.com

W9-AXZ-876

Hope's Bright Promise
Beverly J. Anderson

I wandered down a wooded path;
The wind was brisk and cold.
My winter-weary heart longed for
The spring days to unfold.

And then, with sweet surprise, I saw
A crocus blooming fair,
A purple bloom with frosted lace,
Catching the sunbeams there.

This purple flower in the snow
Cheered up my heart today
With hope's bright promise that the spring
Would soon be on its way.

I pondered how it came to be,
The crocus blooming there,
Mid bleakness and the snowy ground,
Braving the winter air.

How could this tender little shoot
Push up from frozen sod?
I think it was a miracle—
The helping hand of God.

*The bright faces of pansies bring their special cheer,
in spite of lingering snow, to those chilly days of early spring.
Photograph by Fred Habegger/Grant Heilman.*

The Seed Catalog Arrives
Anne Campbell

Outside, the winds of March blow bitterly;
The winter is not over, though I yearn
For daffodils to trip across the lea
And violets to breathe of spring's return.

Idly I turn the pages of this book—
Here delphiniums are bravely blue;
Upon pink Canterbury bells I look
And on the lily of the valley too.

I turn a page and winter fades away
Beneath the glory of a pictured rose.
The skies of March are overcast and gray,
But here beneath my gaze a garden grows.

FROM AMERICA'S ATTIC

Kelly Riley Baugh

SEED CATALOGS

It is a sunny late February day in Middle Tennessee. My two-year-old son and I wear our winter coats as we walk down the drive to the mailbox, his mittened hand in mine. The ground is hard and cold beneath our feet, but there are warm patches where the sun hits the dirt. I look at the poplars in our front yard and see the promise of green in their branches.

At the end of the driveway, I lift my son to the mailbox. Smiling, he pulls the box open and sticks his arm inside. "Flower!" he says, as he pulls out a shiny seed catalog with a bright orange zinnia on the front cover.

We return to the house more slowly than we left it. I turn the pages of the catalog, pausing every few minutes to lean down and show a picture to my son.

My son and I share this happy moment of anticipation because of the hard work of one man

---

Images in early seed catalogs were original works of art.

---

who believed that American gardens could be as beautiful and as productive as those of Europe. W. Atlee Burpee spent many years traveling, observing, and studying, in the late 1800s, and this resulted in his company bringing a better quality and range of seeds to his customers. Burpee's vision helped shape the course of American agriculture.

As a result of his yearly travels to the European continent, Burpee was able to determine that the best fruits and vegetable breeders were German, Dutch, and Scandinavian; the best flower breeders were in England. As Burpee traveled abroad, he kept meticulous notes and made written observations about his findings in a field book. Upon his return to America, Burpee would clean and test the seeds he had purchased, making decisions about which could be successfully adapted to the climate variations of America. In 1888, Burpee established a farm near Doylestown, Pennsylvania, and it soon became a famous development facility. His studies and his field book evolved into the yearly catalog, first named the *Burpee Farm Annual*. The fastest-growing seed company in the United States soon became a dependable and popular business, fulfilling the advertising slogan first used in the 1890s: "Burpee's Seeds Grow."

The early catalog would have provided farmers and gardeners with "new directions for culture," as well as vivid descriptions and pictures of the flowers and produce that could result from planting their seeds. After farmers read about the "wonderful, new, dwarf, meaty, bright-red, earliest tomato," it might have been difficult for them to resist mailing in a seed order.

Images in early seed catalogs were original works of art. Fruits and vegetables were depicted in several art media, including intricate woodcuts, drawings, and watercolors. Cherubs or young women often appeared on the catalog's front cover near the harvest. For example, the 1901 Burpee catalog cover displays three cherub figures holding a plate filled with fruits and vegetables. Underneath the picture are the words "Seed-Sense." Occasionally, animals such as sheep or cattle, or even horses and dogs, were pictured on the covers.

In the 1930s and 1940s, the flowers, lettuce, cabbage, cauliflower, grapes, and other produce included in the catalog were drawn with more realistic proportions. In the 1950s, catalogs began to use photographs rather than drawings. Occasionally, as in Burpee's 1997 catalog, a nostalgic design is presented. The delicate drawing and flowing lines reflect the early traditions of the *Farm Annual.*

For many Americans, a vegetable garden has become a hobby rather than a necessity. But carefully patting down the dirt around fragile sprouts and dampening the soil nourish the spirit, just as the fresh fruits and vegetables nourish the body. While the produce aisle of a grocery or a neighbor's roadside stand can generate the ingredients for the evening meal, they cannot offer a partnership in the miracle of growth. And participation in this partnership is important to me to pass on to my son.

On this early spring day, the changes in the garden landscape herald the new season. Purple and gold top the green leaves of the crocus plants along our front sidewalk. Our irises seem to grow taller by the hour, and their tightly wrapped buds

The back cover of the 1902 Burpee catalog features a giant pepper and green beans. Image courtesy of W. Atlee Burpee Company, Philadelphia, Pennsylvania.

An inside page from the 1895 Burpee catalog features a petunia and carnations. Image courtesy of W. Atlee Burpee Company, Philadelphia, Pennsylvania.

are ready to unfurl. The azalea bushes thicken with green, and their white and pink blossoms will add beauty to our Easter Sunday.

My son, his red toy shovel clasped firmly, and I, with my well-used one, kneel in front of a deep, dark brown square of dirt. Using the tips of our shovels we make tiny trenches in our small plot. He knows what comes next and excitedly lays down his shovel to reach inside the brown willow basket between us. I recognize a faint but unmistakable sound of spring: the rattle of seeds inside thin paper packets.

Kelly Baugh is a book editor at Ideals Publications. She lives in Brentwood, Tennessee, with her husband, son, and two Pembroke Welsh corgis.

Sweet Renewal

Susanna Conner

In early March, melting snow streams off our barn's tin roof and feeds the rivulets winding down the muddy driveway toward the pond. The ducks splash in the sheets of water shimmering on the spongy ice.

This morning I walked through the sugar bush, where our maples grow amid oaks and sassafras. I snapped a maple twig, and a sparkling bead of sap swelled and fell onto the snow blanketing the tree roots. Maple sugaring season had arrived; and for my family, a new farm year had begun.

The miracle of sugaring ensnared my husband and me over twenty-five years ago, and we still enjoy capturing the first run. We are eager to shed the weariness of late winter and embrace the renewing spirit of spring. Out in the barn, we stack sap buckets, lids, and spiles onto our bobsled. He rumbles off on the tractor, but I walk in the tractor's tracks and watch the bluebirds flitting through the orchard. The sun has stripped the last scraps of snow off my garden and exposed the green blades of early daffodils.

Standing beneath a broad maple, my husband turns the brace and the drill licks out bits of bark and wood. Sap begins to ooze into the small hole and then gushes down the trunk. I tap in a spile and slip a metal bucket crowned with a tin roof onto it. *Plink, plink.* Sap strikes the bucket's bottom—the closer the drips, the swifter the flow. We work our way through the sugar bush and the melody from the buckets follows us.

"It's going to be a great year," my husband comments as he gazes at the acres of blueberries growing at the edge of the woods. The chickadees flutter nearby and seem to concur with his forecast as they inspect our work.

As our household begins to celebrate this spring ritual, family and friends splash up the driveway and offer their help. Our octogenarian friend, Rich, stokes the wood fire beneath the evaporator so that John and I can collect sap. Other friends and their children snatch buckets and race from tree to tree.

We are on a treasure hunt, not only for sap, but also for the increasing signs of spring. Opossum tracks, like five petal flowers, wind a trail on the crusty snow beneath the trees. Tiny violets fleck the forest floor in sheltered pockets. Flocks of sandhill cranes wheel overhead and cry, while we dump the sap into the holding tank. A few people ride the bobsled back and risk a drenching from splashing sap, but most of us march through the mud to the sugar shed.

Boiling sap means sticky everything—mittens, jackets; even our hair feels sugary.

Steam billows from the vent in the shed's roof, and the moist air smells like maple candy. Boiling sap means sticky everything—mittens, jackets; even our hair feels sugary.

These are the days to enjoy beans, boiled in sap and baked in syrup, and biscuits covered with melting maple cream. We share these treats with our guests, and they each leave with a jar of warm syrup.

Suddenly the spiles are dry, the buckets silent. As we wash up the equipment and stack it in the barn, the spring peepers sing to us. May apples begin to unfurl their umbrellas beneath the sugar maples, whose swollen buds spread a red mantel across the canopy of the woods. And on our pantry shelves rest rows of Mason jars filled with amber syrup to sweeten the coming farm year.

Maple sap buckets collect the first sweet gift of spring on Canaan Street, in New Hampshire. Photograph by William H. Johnson.

Shall, then, the maple yield sugar, and not man? Shall the farmer be thus active and surely have so much sugar to show for it, before this very March is gone, while I read the newspaper?

While he works in the sugar camp let me work in mine—for sweetness is in me, and to sugar it shall come—it shall not all go to leaves and wood. Am I not a maple sugar man, then?

Boil down the sweet sap which the spring causes to flow within you. Stop not at syrup—go on to sugar, though you present the world with but a single crystal—a crystal not made from trees in your yard, but from the new life that stirs in your pores.

Cheerfully skim your kettle and watch it set and crystallize, making a holiday of it if you will. Heaven will be propitious to you as to him.

—HENRY DAVID THOREAU

COUNTRY CHRONICLE

Lansing Christman

A NEW WORLD

I am ready for spring, ready to be free of ice and snow and cold, biting winds, the short days and long nights. I am ready to see the hills and valleys green again, the streams free of ice and singing on their way to the sea.

I saw the winter birds at the feeders. I heard their chirps and trills. I am ready now for the spring birdsongs of the bluebird and robin, and the gabble of the geese flying in V formation high overhead.

Buds on trees and bushes are feeling the warmth of spring, feeling the urge to burst into bloom. I see spring in the early blooms on crocus and daffodil, the red spires of alders in the marsh, the blooms of the pussy willows in the swamp.

I am waiting for the peepers to tune the swamps and bogs into a symphony of ringing bells, music for the early evening hours, reaching far into the nights.

Spring is yielding its longer hours of sun, bringing a warmth that is so much like an arm of friendship around my shoulders, like a face of affection pressed to mine, the warmth of a hand clasping mine.

I am ready for the renewal of life that comes each year with the vernal season, bringing a whole new world to my countryside.

The author of four books, Lansing Christman has contributed to Ideals for more than thirty years. Mr. Christman has also been published in several American, international, and braille anthologies. He lives in rural South Carolina.

Birdhouses and flowers brighten a table set for breakfast.
Photograph by Jessie Walker.

Song of Spring
Mildred L. Jarrell

Oh, I have heard a robin sing
This lovely early morn,
Announcing once again to all
Another spring is born.

He seeks the same old nesting place
In the side-yard maple tree
And will trust us with the secret
Of his little family.

His song is carried by the breeze
To waken springtime flowers,
Who peep with gladness on a world
A-greening with spring showers.

My heart rejoices to the tune
His early tidings bring;
I know that spring has come at last,
For I heard a robin sing.

Cadenzas
Jane Bassett Fox

An *a capella* chorus of birds awakened me
though they were hidden—their stage I could not see—
with a vibrato trill at the end of each beat
and a rhapsody of cadenzas and an occasional repeat.
They must have been singing to birdies in the nest,
for in some sonatas there was a crooning tenderness.

As I was listening, I couldn't help but think
how wonderful it would be if we were as content;
and little daily pleasures brought into our lives a song;
and we were virtuosos who sang solos all day long.

Apple blossoms shimmer in the sunlight in Door County, Wisconsin.
Photograph by Darryl R. Beers.

BIRD-VOICES

Nathaniel Hawthorne

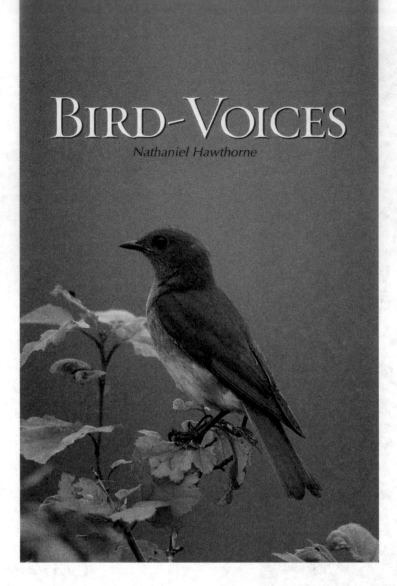

Among the delights of spring, how is it possible to forget the birds? Even the crows were welcome, as the sable harbingers of a brighter and livelier race. They visited us before the snow was off, but seem mostly to have betaken themselves to remote depths of the woods, which they haunt all summer long. Many a time shall I disturb them there and feel as if I had intruded among a company of silent worshipers as they sit in Sabbath stillness among the treetops.

Their voices, when they speak, are in admirable accordance with the tranquil solitude of a summer afternoon, and, resounding so far above the head, their loud clamor increases the religious quiet of the scene instead of breaking it. A crow, however, has no real pretensions to religion, in spite of his gravity of mien and black attire; he is certainly a thief, and probably an infidel.

The gulls are far more respectable, in a moral point of view. These denizens of sea-beaten rocks and haunters of the lonely beach come up our inland river at this season and soar high overhead, flapping their broad wings in the upper sunshine. They are among the most picturesque of birds because they so float and rest upon the air as to become almost stationary parts of the landscape. The imagination has time to grow acquainted with them; they have not flitted away in a moment. . . .

The smaller birds—the little songsters of the woods and those that haunt man's dwellings and claim human friendship by building their nests under the sheltering eaves or among the orchard trees—these require a touch more delicate and a gentler heart than mine to do them justice. Their outburst of melody is like a brooklet loose from wintry chains. We need not deem it a too high and solemn word to call it a hymn of praise to the Creator, since Nature, who pictures the reviving year in so many sights of beauty, has expressed the sentiment of renewed life in no other sound save the notes of these blessed birds.

consort together—are the noisiest of all our feathered citizens. Great companies of them—more than the famous "four-and-twenty" whom Mother Goose has immortalized—congregate in contiguous treetops and vociferate with all the clamor and confusion of a turbulent political meeting. Politics, certainly, must be the occasion of such tumultuous debates, but still, unlike all other politicians, they instill melody into their individual utterances and produce harmony as a general effect.

Of all bird-voices, none are more sweet and cheerful to my ear than those of swallows in the dim, sun-streaked interior of a lofty barn; they

WILL THE WORLD EVER BE SO DECAYED THAT SPRING MAY NOT RENEW ITS GREENNESS?

Their music, however, just now seems to be incidental and not the result of a set purpose. They are discussing the economy of life and love and the site and architecture of their summer residences, and have no time to sit on a twig and pour forth solemn hymns or overtures, operas, symphonies, and waltzes. Anxious questions are asked, grave subjects are settled in quick and animated debate, and, only by occasional accident as from pure ecstasy, does a rich warble roll its tiny waves of golden sound through the atmosphere.

Their little bodies are as busy as their voices; they are in a constant flutter and restlessness. Even when two or three retreat to a treetop to hold council, they wag their tails and heads all the time with irrepressible activity of their nature, which perhaps renders their brief span of life in reality as long as the patriarchal age of sluggish man.

The blackbirds—three species of which

address the heart with even a closer sympathy than Robin Redbreast. . . .

Thank Providence for spring! The earth—and man himself, by sympathy with his birthplace—would be far other than we find them if life toiled wearily onward without this periodical infusion of the primal spirit. Will the world ever be so decayed that spring may not renew its greenness? Can man be so dismally age-stricken that no faintest sunshine of his youth may revisit him once a year? It is impossible.

Summer works in the present and thinks not of the future; autumn is a rich conservative; winter has utterly lost its faith and clings tremulously to the remembrance of what has been; but spring, with its outgushing life, is the true type of the movement.

An eastern bluebird poses in brief perfection.
Photograph by Arthur C. Smith/Grant Heilman.

Rebirth
Susan Lent

The morning is as fresh and fragile
    as a broken eggshell,
The inside world cushioned
    in a film of fine, pale gold.
If you would see the mystery
    of rebirth, come softly,
For God walks in the silence
    with the new day in His hands.

Morning Miracle
Linda Watkins-Richardson

As morning rises gently overnight
    and trees stretch limbs to the waking sun;
as dew purifies yesterday's storms
    and a bright new day is ushered in;
as fresh currents flow from a river's soul
    and soil is overturned within,
I know that change comes with each day.
    I know my life can change today.

Wake-Up Call
Mary Catherine Johnson

Like reluctant waking sleepers, loathe to greet the dawn of day,
The winter woodlands drowse in somber hues of gray,
Closely clutching tiny buds that struggle to be free
To fling their spring-green foliage onto each lazy tree.
But spring will not stay secret, though the boughs may not be green.
Unbridled blossoms burst abloom and suddenly are seen
Throughout the wood, suspended in the forest dim and drear,
The dogwoods' starry clusters proclaim, "Spring is here!"

A Western dogwood blooms on the banks of the North Umpqua River in Umpqua National Forest, Oregon. Photograph by Mary Liz Austin/Donnelly Austin Photography.

Above: This detail of flowering bunchberry (dwarf dogwood) shows two delicate blooms. Photograph by Terry Donnelly/Donnelly Austin Photography.

BACKYARD CALENDAR

Joan Donaldson

I open my garden gate and breathe the scent of sun-warmed soil, freshly tilled and damp. A weathered, board fence encloses neat beds waiting to be planted with onion sets and seed potatoes. Dozens of old roses—damask, galica, and moss—hug the lichen-encrusted boards. On this sheltered piece of earth, I feel like the ancient Celts, that I am standing in a "thin spot" where heaven and earth join hands. Just as my Savior went to a garden to pray, I come here not only to plant, but to reap moments that revive my spirit.

Hope abounds in my awakening garden. The grassy paths are still matted from the heavy load of January's drifted snow; but in a corner, ivory flecks the grass where small white violets hint at the harvest and beauty that will flourish in the upcoming months. Sap rising in the twigs of the roses brings a fresh green to the bushes and swells the leaf buds. Come June, Charles de Mills and La Reine Victoria will perfume the air while my Seven Sisters cascades over the garden's arching gateway.

My own pulse quickens with the smells and sights of spring transforming what looked so barren only a few weeks ago. Each day brings changes at this time of the year.

This morning, the wrinkled leaves of the rhubarb inch out of the soil, and the knobby roots of the peonies unfurl maroon feathers. Yellow flashes between the slats in the fence where clusters of daffodils bloom. A patch of chervil gleams at the end of the strawberry bed. I love these emerging plants for reminding me that spring triumphs no matter how bitter winter's gloom.

I hear claws scraping on wood, and our white-and-gray-striped cat, Spencer, scrambles over the fence. Some sixth sense alerts him to join me whenever I enter this domain. He sniffs at a rosette of catnip poking up beneath a rosebush, but its leaves have not gained their tantalizing fragrance. Like all good things, they need time and nurturing in order to thrive.

The whisper of wings draws my eyes upward from the dirt, and a silent trio of swans sails overhead, sunlight shimmering on their feathers.

Spencer plops down by a clump of Johnny-jump-ups and purrs. His lettuce-green eyes follow my hands as I dig a shallow trough for peas with a garden fork. I rip open the seed packet, the paper still crisp. Methodically, I drop the light green beads, so full of potential, into the furrow. *Splat!* Spencer springs and scatters the seeds. Rolling about, he smashes dirt over the row of peas. I shake my head and tickle his tummy. I have learned to accept these little interruptions and other challenges that bump into my day. Eventually, Spencer curls up in my gardening basket and naps.

The whisper of wings draws my eyes upward from the dirt, and a silent trio of swans sails overhead, sunlight shimmering on their feathers. They fly toward the river where generations of fowl have nested. A tufted titmouse calls: "Peter! Peter!" from the branches of an apple tree that extend over my garden fence. All of nature feels the rhythm of spring that stirs new life into creation.

I pat down the soil over the buried peas and dust off my hands, a simple task that unites me with countless other gardeners throughout the centuries. I snap off a couple of sassafras twigs to mark the rows. I know a late snow will dust their resting place and that I will give in to the temptation to dig up a few seeds so that I can discover if any are sprouting. But God's faithfulness will never fail me. In His timing, tiny green wings will unfold into sturdy seedlings that will send spiraling trendrils heavenward.

Morning by morning, I will find joy in this place where heaven and earth meet.

Joan Donaldson is the author of a picture book and a young adult novel, as well as essays that have appeared in many national publications. She and her husband raised their sons on Pleasant Hill Farm in Michigan, where they continue to practice rural skills.

Tribute to Gardeners
Roy Z. Kemp

Who plants a flower garden
Is very blessed, indeed;
He has a love for beauty
That fills a vital need.
But he who has a garden
And digs deep in the sod,
Then plants the seed for making bread,
Lives very close to God.

What a Garden Knows
Revah Summersgill

What has a garden seen and heard
Besides the flashing songs of birds
And the colorful blossoms that lean and sway
With the kindly wind in a graceful way?

What does a garden know but peace
And fruitfulness and glad increase,
What but bloom and tranquil sun
And a harvesting when summer's done?

Any garden that is ever grown
To full ripening also knows
Worm and weed and storms and blight
And the frost at last, some wintry night.

The cycle of birth and growth and death
Is compassed in any flower's breath.
But a garden knows too that another spring
Will rise out of each snow's covering!

God Almighty first planted a garden. And indeed it is the purest of human pleasures. It is the greatest refreshment to the spirits of man, without which buildings and palaces are but gross handiworks.
—Sir Francis Bacon

This potting shed invites a gardener to begin spring tasks with joy. Photograph by Jessie Walker.

19

Forsythia

Milly Walton

A Midas touch has changed the bush
That yesterday was brown and bare;
As if by magic, fragile sprays
Of gilded bells sway on the air.

Atoning for their tardy leaves,
They blossom with a lavish grace,

Embroidering spring's chartreuse gown
With filigree of yellow lace.

Such spendthrift loveliness is brief,
Elusive as a fleeting dream;
Remember, then, forsythia
And treasure its pale gold gleam.

Growing Sunbeams

Becky Jennings

Like a golden, sunlit fountain,
Petals burst into radiant bloom,
Brightening the springtime garden
Or gladdening a dreary room.

Each bloom is a tiny sunbeam;
Each bough an amber delight,

Enchanting all the outside
With delicate blossoms so bright.

It cascades over pale green grass
In calm ripples of molten gold;
What a lovely treat in early spring
To watch forsythia unfold.

The land all around was yellow with bloom,
The birds in the branches sang joyous and shrill,
The blue range rose 'gainst the blue of the sky.
FRANCES TYRRELL GILL

The golden branches of forsythia in this pansy garden herald the first blossoms of spring. Photograph by William H. Johnson.

Tulips

J. Harold Gwynne

In March they push up brownish spears,
Then flare out leaves like rabbit ears!
Then tall and stately stems arise,
As gentle rain falls from the skies.
Mid-April sees their cups unfold—
The pink, the scarlet, white, and gold.
What beauty glows in every cup,
When tulips lift each chalice up!

The Coming of Spring

Kay Hoffman

When the days begin to lengthen,
   And winter's on the wing,
Nothing cheers my heart as much
   As the coming of the spring.

I wait with sweet expectancy
   To hear the robin's song,
While the sun-warmed little brooklet
   Bobs happily along.

Bright daffodils and tulips nod
   Along the garden way;
The fragrance sweet of lilacs near
   Makes heavenly my day.

On a hill nearby, a dogwood tree
   Is gloriously abloom,
And in my heart it seems that I
   Am in the Upper Room.

I lift my eyes to heaven
   Toward skies so blue and clear;
Consider how a springtime day
   Can bring God's presence near.

Tulip Days

Nora M. Bozeman

As spring unfolds her tulip days
And spins her golden sun-drenched rays,
I see a graceful dogwood tree
Dressed in lacy filigree.
The dewy morn smells fresh and clean;
The lawn is lush and vibant green;
Wildflowers pop up in excess,
Displaying blooms of loveliness.
Daylight dawns in dew-dropped mist;
The silvered moon is starlight-kissed;
And God His heavenly music plays,
As spring unfolds her tulip days.

A perennial garden in Prescott Park, Portsmouth, New Hampshire, has a chorus of brightly colored tulips to welcome visitors. Photograph by William H. Johnson.

Above: An exquisite tulip, named Blushing Beauty, is one of the many jewels of spring. Photograph by Jessie Walker.

Miracles
Anne Penrod

In spring, we plant our tiny seeds
And hope that they will grow.
Amazingly, they thrive and sprout;
But how, we do not know.
We water them and give them sun;
We fertilize the soil.
We are never sure if we shall see
Results for all our toil.
Then, as our flowers bud and bloom
We know—we don't surmise—
That miracles are possible.
They are right before our eyes.

My Garden
Ruth O. Brown

Fashioned by the hand of time
My garden beckons me,
As I take a book and go to sit
Beneath the weeping willow tree.

The flowers are in their colorful dress,
Enticing me to stay,
As I walk along the well-worn path
Into scenes of yesterday.

The birds are singing in the trees,
Providing a note of mirth,
And I'd rather be in this enchanted place
Than anywhere on earth.

Lines Written in Early Spring
William Wordsworth

Through primrose tufts, in that green bower,
The periwinkle trailed its wreaths;
And 'tis my faith that every flower
Enjoys the air it breathes.

The birds around me hopped and played,
Their thoughts I cannot measure—

But the least motion which they made
It seemed a thrill of pleasure.

The budding twigs spread out their fan,
To catch the breezy air;
And I must think, do all I can,
That there was pleasure there.

The pastel hues of wisteria and rhododendron blooms are the perfect accessories for this brightly painted home in Yamhill County, Oregon. Photograph by Steve Terrill.

Overleaf: A Japanese Garden in Portland, Oregon, offers a beautiful, reflective place for visitors. Photograph by Jon Gnass/Gnass Photo Images.

The Beauty of All Springs

Jessie Merle Franklin

The morning is as fresh as the drummed-in milk
Left foaming in a bucket. Hooves cut dents
In the worn cow trail along which dew-wet silk
Of spider crochet sparkles on the fence.
The small girl ties the gate against the hill
And, parting thick growth, peers in where a birch
Stands slim and straight like a spire. The sun lies still
As if it shines through the windows of a church.
There is neither sound nor stir—no startled hare,
No rustling life, no sudden flap of wings—
Only the beating heart of a child aware
Of Him who makes the beauty of all springs.

The spring over there
takes you by the throat,
the flowers blooming by
the thousands over white walls.
If you strolled around for an
hour in the hills surrounding my
town, you would return with the
odor of honey in your clothes.

—Albert Camus

A young lady relaxes with an adoring collie and a pet fawn in this painting by Robert Walker MacBeth (1848–1910), entitled Fair Pledges of a Fruitful Tree. *Image from Fine Art Photographic Library, Ltd., London/ Fine Art of Oakham.*

Pansy Garden
Mary M. Hamilton

Kneeling in this fragrant place,
I would touch each elfin face;
Golden brown and creamy white
Shimmer in the summer light.
Here, a purple velvet cloak,
Such a fancy might evoke
For the robe of fairy folk.
Every blossom wears a smile;
Had I sorrow to beguile,
Needed strength for weary while,
Kneeling in this fragrant place,
I would touch each elfin face.

Pansies
Julia C. Laib

There's the sweetest bed of pansies
    growing in my garden fair,
Quite surpassing all the other flowers
    that happen to be there.
In their tiny upturned faces,
    all so winsome and so shy,
There is something so alluring
    that we cannot pass them by;
But we gaze with admiration
    at the rare and beauteous shades
Of the dainty little coquettes
    nodding there on dress parade.

Who can resist smiling at purple pansy faces? Photograph by Dianne Dietrich Leis/Dietrich Leis Stock Photography.

BITS & PIECES

Blossom by blossom
the spring begins.
—*Algernon Charles Swinburne*

How fresh, O Lord, how sweet and clean
Are Thy returns! Ev'n as the flowers in Spring.
—*George Herbert*

Spring unlocks
the flowers to paint
the laughing soil.
—*Reginald Heber*

Ah, life, what is it but a flower?
—*A. E. Housman*

Twine thy brows with fresh spring flowers
And call a train of laughing Hours.
—*William Wordsworth*

Our gardens are enamored of the spring,
Of silver rain,
The cloudy green of buds' slow-burgeoning.
—*Walter Adolphe Roberts*

Spring's tender blossoms, buds and leaves,
The sisterhood of flowers.
—*George Pope Morris*

Here comes the time when,
vibrating on its stem, every flower
fumes like a censer; noises and
perfumes circle in the evening air.
—*Charles Baudelaire*

And warming in the sun
Shy flowers began to peer.
—*Robert Kelley Weeks*

God's bright and intricate device
Of days and seasons doth suffice.
—*Robert Louis Stevenson*

The buds awake at touch of Spring
From Winter's joyless dream.
—*Mackenzie Bell*

THROUGH MY WINDOW

Pamela Kennedy

BOTANICAL BATTLES

It is spring again. In mainland gardens, crocuses and daffodils are blooming. Tulips nod their regal heads in acknowledgment of the freshening breezes, and buds and blossoms fill the air with fragrance. Even though we lack the changing seasons here in Hawaii, fragrant blossoms perfume the air and baskets and buckets of annuals beckon at the garden shops. Shoppers haul home topsoil and fertilizer in expectation of beautiful blooms. But not me. Not any more. I have finally surrendered my trowel on the botanical battlefield.

I did not come to this place in my life haphazardly. No, it was a deliberate decision based on many years of experimentation and self-examination. Let me begin by saying that my problem is not genetic. My mother could grow anything from azaleas to zinnias. She planted hills of cucumbers and beans that fed us for months. And her fruit trees produced buckets of apples, pears, cherries, and plums. But the years I planted vegetables, the slugs and rabbits got to them. Squirrels dug up my tulip bulbs, and my few daffodils that made it to daylight were quickly nibbled by passing deer. I tried all kinds of border and bedding plants that were supposed to be impervious to insects and rot, but something always attacked their leaves and blossoms once they hit the dirt in my yard.

So I took my efforts indoors. Envious of a friend's beautiful African violets, I bought a few plants and placed them on a friendly looking windowsill. Within a couple of weeks, my windowsill was littered with faded lavender blossoms. I tried ferns and ivy, but they failed too, their crispy brown leaves dropping long before fall.

I decided to turn over a new leaf (so to

---

*I knew when to raise the white flag.
It was time to forget about horticulture.*

---

speak). In a fit of creative energy, one winter afternoon I actually designed a plant made entirely from green flannel. It really was something to see. I inserted long wires along the edges of the huge leaves so that they could be bent into what I considered "lifelike" poses. But my "flannel filodendron" only lasted until our toddler dismantled it. I moved up to silk flowers and plants. These, I discovered, were the perfect solution to my dilemma. They never had to be watered, placed in the sun, watched for bugs, or tempted with fancy fertilizers. And when we moved, which we did often during twenty-eight years in the Navy, they just went into cartons with the rest of our household goods. But my surrender to silk was not quite complete.

When my husband retired from the Navy and was offered a civilian job in Hawaii, we bought a home which had a small garden that could be viewed from a glass-enclosed entryway. So I decided to try one more time.

I talked with several folks down at the garden store about which flowers were the hardiest and would grow best in partial shade. I surreptitiously checked out my neighbors' yards for healthy looking specimens. Then I planned my little strip of garden. I bought topsoil and products that promised my garden would be miraculous. I spaded and watered and fertilized and put out a beautiful row of flowering plants surrounded by groundcover that was supposed to grow into a "lush carpet of tiny blooms nestled in deep green foliage."

For several days I gazed at my beautiful garden, willing it to be healthy and abundant with blossoms and leaves. Then, one morning, I looked out through the entryway windows and gasped. Every single blossom and about half of the leaves were gone! Little bare stems stuck up out of the soil, surrounded by a maze of snail and slug trails. That did it. I knew when to raise the white flag. It was time to forget about horticulture.

That weekend I took the van to the garden store and bought a quarter ton of river rocks. I laid down plastic ground cloth and began dumping my rocks onto it. With the larger ones, I created a little border that enclosed the twenty-foot length of my former garden, and, with the smaller ones, I designed a "stream" running through the larger rocks. I set a couple of concrete stumps at the end of the stream, like fallen logs; I bought a plaster bird and placed it on one stump and put a little concrete boy with a fishing pole at a curve in the stream.

I found a small iron bridge to span a narrow place and a ceramic turtle to bask in the sun. No slugs were tempted to sully my garden, and no snails even ventured near its rocky shore.

Every day my little rock garden remains the same, flowing faithfully under its bridge, past the stoic turtle and the faithful bird. It does equally well in sun and rain, needs no care, and never fades or withers. It's a garden for all seasons. And this spring, when my neighbors' gardens bloom with color, I will sit indoors, content at last with my silk plants and trees, enjoying the unchanging beauty of my stony stream.

Pamela Kennedy is a freelance writer of short stories, articles, essays, and children's books. Wife of a retired naval officer and mother of three children, she has made her home on both U.S. coasts and currently resides in Honolulu, Hawaii.

Original artwork by Doris Ettlinger.

The skies can't keep their secret!
They tell it to the hills—
The hills just tell the orchards—
And they the daffodils!
—EMILY DICKINSON

Where Beauty Lies
May Smith White

I must go back to see the jonquils bloom
Along the garden path I knew so well,
For there I can forget the thoughts that loom
Like crumbling walls of some old citadel.
So few the years, yet with them much has passed
That lent me warmth and melted winter's snow.
I must go back, I must go back at last
To taste the wind where April jonquils blow.

Wind Song
Mary Shirley Krouse

The wind went waltzing up Gypsy Lane
And singing up Strawberry Hill.
It knocked "hello" on the windowpane
And then teased a young daffodil.

It rode the clouds like a carousel
And climbed to the sun to kiss her.
It dusted the fields in the farmer's dell
And crossed the creek on a whisper.

Playing tag with the leaves on the roofs
And sailing our kites up high,
Prancing about on feathery hoofs,
The wind sang a song to the sky.

Singular Gold
Edith G. Schay

One buttercup
Is more exciting than a score.
One buttercup!
The young heart drinks its beauty up;
The old heart seeks an open door
Where it may lean and see, once more,
One buttercup.

*Spring's arrival at Morosani Farm in Litchfield,
Connecticut, is announced by fields of daffodils.
Photograph by William H. Johnson.*

*Inset: Two daffodil blooms offer yellow perfection
on a sunny spring day. Photograph by Dianne Dietrich
Leis/Dietrich Leis Stock Photography.*

SLICE OF LIFE

Edna Jaques

APRIL

The wind is whispering April
    And the woods are all aflame.
Today a robin sang for me;
    From southern lands he came.
He brought the springtime with his song
    And practiced it the whole day long.

The sun is whispering April
    And the buds are swelling green.
The little creek is running wild
    Its foolish banks between;
The pussy willow's silver fur
    Is making vain the heart of her.

And we have tidied all the yard,
    Raked up the tangled grass;
The little pool that father made
    Shines like a looking glass—
Reflecting sky and clouds and trees,
    The neighbors' clothesline, if you please.

The wind is whispering April
    And all my heart is knowing
There will be clover in the fields
    And new grass growing,
Daffodils on a sturdy stem,
    And golden bees to talk to them.

READERS' REFLECTIONS

Readers are invited to submit original poetry for possible publication in future issues of IDEALS. *Please send typed copies only; manuscripts will not be returned. Writers receive payment for each published submission. Send material to Readers' Reflections, Ideals Publications, 535 Metroplex Drive, Suite 250, Nashville, Tennessee 37211.*

God's Garden

Eleanor Anderson
Sherwood, Oregon

See the hills and valleys
Covered deep with snow;
Feel the warm rays of the sun
On this, His world below;
Smell the fragrance of the flowers;
Know that God above
Sends us down His blessings,
A garden of His love.

An April Day

Evalyn Torrant
Midland, Michigan

At dawn the doves sit still as boulders,
With heads retracted into shoulders.
The grass, new-minted green and bright,
Gleams hoary, whitened overnight,
While tulip rows, once proud and tall,
Bow supple as a waterfall.

But noon will bring another scene:
The doves will peck and grass re-green.
Each tulip stalk will straighten up
To drink light from its silken cup.
For spring again must have its way
And April blossom into May.

I Believe in Spring

Ralph Nunn
Independence, Missouri

I'll always believe
That winter's cold chill
Can again be broken
By spring's eternal will.

While crocuses are blooming
Through the melting snow,
The daffodils break forth
And their buds start to grow.

Swollen high creeks
Boil chocolate brown,
While honest labor
Waits to till the ground.

I know it's coming;
I won't have to wait long
For spring's first robin
To break out in song.

The spring wind knows
What my thoughts can conceive,
As it whispers the dream
That I believe.

Spring Sightings

Naomi R. Hicks
West Linn, Oregon

The day is warm and washed with light;
Four lovely snow peaks are in sight;
The garden scenes and smells invite—
It's spring and life looks great.

The birds enjoy the flowers, too—
Some darting hummers come in view
To sip the nectar, drink the dew;
Their blurred wings captivate.

The gentle sounds of birds and bees,
The swaying tips of tall fir trees
In counterpoint to sighing breeze
Are music to the ears.

This season signals the end of cold;
As sprouting seeds and flowers unfold,
A miracle once more is told:
New life will reappear.

HOMETOWN AMERICA

Elizabeth Raum

MAIN STREET
BRATTLEBORO, VERMONT

In the 1890s, English writer Rudyard Kipling spent three years living in Brattleboro, Vermont, my hometown. He wrote *Captains Courageous* and *The Jungle Books* while living at Naulaka, his Brattleboro home. When he returned to England in 1894, he wrote a friend: "A regular weather-breeder of a day to-day–real warmth at last and it waked in me a lively desire to be back in Main Street, Brattleboro, Vermont, USA."

I was born in Brattleboro nearly sixty years after Kipling left, but I share his fascination with Main Street. As a child I looked forward to Friday night trips downtown. We bought our groceries at the First National, shopped at Mann's for clothing and fabrics, and purchased vitamins and cold remedies at the Hotel Pharmacy. Several sporting goods stores sold skates, sleds, and ski equipment.

My brothers and I spent our allowance on toys or books at Woolworth's, treats at Grant's soda fountain, or a Saturday matinee at the Paramount or Latchis. Both theaters retained the elegance of silent movies days, and the price of a ticket allowed us to sit through several showings of the same film.

I had my first encounters with the literary life among the nooks and crannies of the Brooks

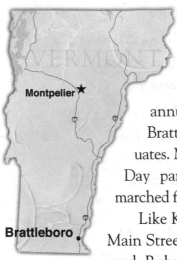

Memorial Library. A twisting stairway led to the Children's Room furnished with dark mahogany bookshelves, pint-sized furniture, and enough books to keep me reading for years.

Main Street was filled with delights. It was a busy, active place. Traffic clogged the intersections, pedestrians gathered to visit on the sidewalks, and parades attracted huge crowds downtown. The annual Alumni Parade celebrated Brattleboro Union High School's graduates. Memorial Day parades, St. Patrick's Day parades, and even circus parades marched from one end of Main to the other.

Like Kipling, I often long to be back on Main Street. Some of the old stores—Brown and Roberts Hardware, Town Pharmacy, Sam's Outfitters, and Baker's Bookstore—continue to thrive. The Latchis Theater, newly restored, shows the latest movies, and the Holstein

---

Volunteers dribbled hot maple syrup over a pan of fresh snow.

Association, the largest cow breeders association in the United States, maintains its headquarters at the foot of Main Street, as it has since 1885.

As a child, I loved the Winter Carnival, held

Naulaka, Rudyard Kipling's home in Vermont, is a popular tourist attraction. Photograph courtesy of The Landmark Trust (U.S.A.).

A favorite downtown landmark, this 1908 electric clock was originally commissioned by businessmen and is now owned by the city. Image courtesy of Brattleboro Chamber of Commerce. Photograph by William Hayes.

mid-February. It used to include a parade of Queen candidates atop fabulous floats and a Sugar-on-Snow party. Volunteers dribbled hot maple syrup over a pan of fresh snow. They served it with a dill pickle, a cake doughnut, and instruc-

---

The Strolling of the Heifers, held annually the first week in June, celebrates Brattleboro's dairy farms.

---

tions to eat the hardened syrup, not the snow. The Carnival, approaching its fiftieth year, still includes a Sugar-on-Snow party, but the parade is now a torch light walk though town with a snowman. A country and western jamboree, variety show, and junior Olympics make the Winter Carnival truly a family event.

Such changes keep Brattleboro lively. The old library is gone, replaced by a newer one filled with current resources. Gourmet restaurants, music stores, art galleries, and gift shops line Main Street. There is even a new parade. The Strolling of the Heifers, held annually the first weekend in June, celebrates Brattleboro's dairy farms. It features dozens of young cows marching up Main. Some march regally. Others must be tugged, pushed, and prodded along by their young owners. In the spirit of the event, some spectators, and even a dog or two, dress up as big black-and-white Holsteins.

Yes, some things have changed since Kipling walked the streets, but locals and visitors alike continue to enjoy the sights and sounds (including the occasional *moo*) of Main Street, Brattleboro, Vermont, USA.

Elizabeth Raum is the author of two books for children and nine books for adults. She lives in Huntington, New York.

Cherry Blossoms

Hilda Butler Farr

I marvel at the miracle of spring
That I may look upon so close at hand,
A miracle destroying doubt and fear,
Renewing faith in all that God has planned.
For only yesterday the land was bare,
And now each time I look at it I see
Some lovely, fragile blossoms added there.
A gorgeous picture is the cherry tree.
But never has it meant as much as now,
When the world is beset by the whims of men.
How can I doubt that God is nearby,
When I observe these blossoms once again.

A Prayer in Spring

Robert Frost

Oh, give us pleasure in the flowers today;
And give us not to think so far away
As the uncertain harvest; keep us here
All simply in the springing of the year.

Oh, give us pleasure in the orchard white,
Like nothing else by day, like ghosts by night;
And make us happy in the happy bees,
The swarm dilating round the perfect trees.

And make us happy in the darting bird
That suddenly above the bees is heard,
The meteor that thrusts in with needle bill,
And off a blossom in mid air stands still.

For this is love and nothing else is love,
The which it is reserved for God above
To sanctify to what far ends He will,
But which it only needs that we fulfill.

Symbol

David Morton

My faith is all a doubtful thing,
    Woven on a doubtful loom—
Until there comes, each showery spring,
    A cherry tree in bloom;
And Christ, who died upon a tree
    That death had stricken bare,
Comes beautifully back to me
    In blossoms everywhere.

*Cherry trees in full bloom line the sidewalk
to a school in Bradford, Connecticut.
Photograph by William H. Johnson.*

Spring Belongs with Easter

Ralph W. Seager

Spring itself is Resurrection!
Bough and bud combine to prove
That death is a temporal imperfection
Through which all of life must move.
From the husk new green arises,
From the kernel roots appear,
And, though our hopes wear dark disguises,
Faith can find its white robes here.

The Path That
Leads to Nowhere

Corinne Roosevelt Robinson

There's a path that leads to Nowhere
    In a meadow that I know,
Where an inland island rises
    And the stream is still and slow;
There it wanders under willows
    And beneath the silver green
Of the birches' silent shadows,
    Where the early violets lean.

There I go to meet the Springtime,
    When the meadow is aglow,
Marigolds amid the marshes,
    And the stream is still and slow;
There I find my fair oasis,
    And with carefree feet I tread;
For the pathway leads to Nowhere
    And the blue is overhead!

All the ways that lead to Somewhere
    Echo with the hurrying feet
Of the Struggling and the Striving,
    But the way I find so sweet
Bids me dream and bids me linger—
    Joy and Beauty are its goal;
On the path that leads to Nowhere
    I have sometimes found my soul!

Black Walnut Nature Trail in Perrot State Park, Trempealeau County, Wisconsin, seems to offer an intriguing choice for a spring morning walk. Photograph by Darryl R. Beers.

On Easter Day

Celia Thaxter

Easter lilies! Can you hear
What they whisper, low and clear?
In dewy fragrance they unfold
Their splendor sweet,
    their snow and gold.
Every beauty-breathing bell
News of heaven has to tell.
Listen to their mystic voice;
Hear, O mortal, and rejoice!
Hark, their soft and heavenly chime:
Christ is risen for all time.

Easter Lily

Catherine Donnelly

Spring touched a snowflake
    that winter had left,
Turning it into a bloom,
With petals fashioned after the wings
Of an angel who sat by the tomb,
Fragrantly scenting the early spring air,
Vibrant with promises given
By Christ, whose victory over the grave
Has opened the doorway to heaven.

Lilies

*Shiko; arranged by
Olive Beaupré Miller*

I thought I saw white clouds, but no!
    Bending across the fence,
    White lilies in a row!

The Lilies of Easter

James H. Boyden

Snow-white petals, waxen smooth,
Frame the pistil's slender shaft,
Proclaiming spring's rebirth anew,
As in the years now past.

Heralds of the Easter dawn:
Faith, unrestrained by strife,
The purity of love, unstained,
The hope, eternal life.

And now may these abide with you,
The gift of Heaven's trinity—
Faith, hope, and love divine
Through time and all eternity.

HOW FAIR AND HOW PURE IS THE LILY!

—Robert Burns

A single Easter lily, pink hydrangea, and tulips make a lovely bouquet. Photograph by Nancy Matthews.

The Church the Garden of Christ

Isaac Watts

We are a garden walled around,
Chosen and made peculiar ground,
A little spot enclosed by grace,
Out of the world's wide wilderness.

Like trees of myrrh and spice we stand,
Planted by God the Father's hand;
And all His springs in Zion flow,
To make the young plantation grow.

Awake, O heavenly wind! and come,
Blow on this garden of perfume;
Spirit divine! Descend and breathe
A gracious gale on plants beneath.

Make our best spices flow abroad,
To entertain our Savior God:
And faith, and love, and joy appear,
And every grace be active here.

*When thy heart says, "Father, pardon!"
Then the Lord is in thy garden.*
—GEORGE MACDONALD

The First Congregational Church, West Tisbury, Martha's Vinyard, Massachusetts, is framed by blue sky, a white fence, and a dogwood in bloom. Photograph by William H. Johnson.

Young Jesus

Sara Henderson Hay

They said that He was meek;
    they were not wrong,
But He was more than meek.
The Christ I know was young
    and bronzed and strong,
Clear-eyed and tanned of cheek.
He wore His valor stoutly, as a shield
Borne to a bloody field.

And He was gentle—
    but the word falls short
Of one lone Man who drove
The moneychangers from
    the temple court.
The Christ I know was brave.
What splendid courage
    made the knotted cords
More terrible than swords!

And He was patient—
    but His lips grew white;
He spoke with God's own wrath,
Whose royal fury put
    the thieves to flight
And scourged them from His path.

Lowly and meek and mild—
    but much more.
He saw, upon that day,
The road to Calvary stretching before
And would not turn away,
Young Jesus, going gallantly to death,
The Man of Nazareth!

*Magnolia blossoms and forsythia in bloom make
a beautiful spring palette. Photograph by
William H. Johnson.*

The Last Supper

Matthew 26:20–21, 26–30

Now when the even was come, He sat down with the twelve. And as they did eat, He said, Verily I say unto you, that one of you shall betray me.

And as they were eating, Jesus took bread and blessed it, and brake it, and gave it to the disciples, and said, Take, eat; this is My body. And He took the cup and gave thanks, and gave it to them, saying, Drink ye all of it; For this is My blood of the new testament, which is shed for many for the remission of sins.

But I say unto you, I will not drink henceforth of this fruit of the vine, until that day when I drink it new with you in my Father's kingdom. And when they had sung an hymn, they went out into the mount of Olives.

THE LAST SUPPER *by Philippe de Champaigne (1602–1674). Image from Art Resource/Louvre. Photograph by Erich Lessing.*

King of the Jews

Matthew 27: 15–30

Now at that feast the governor was wont to release unto the people a prisoner, whom they would. And they had then a notable prisoner, called Barabbas.

Therefore when they were gathered together, Pilate said unto them, Whom will ye that I release unto you? Barabbas, or Jesus which is called Christ? For he knew that for envy they had delivered Him.

When he was set down on the judgment seat, his wife sent unto him, saying, Have thou nothing to do with that just man: for I have suffered many things this day in a dream because of him.

But the chief priests and elders persuaded the multitude that they should ask Barabbas, and destroy Jesus. The governor answered and said unto them, Whether of the twain will ye that I release unto you?

They said, Barabbas.

Pilate saith unto them, What shall I do then with Jesus which is called Christ? They all say unto him, Let Him be crucified.

And the governor said, Why, what evil hath He done? But they cried out the more, saying, Let Him be crucified.

When Pilate saw that he could prevail nothing, but that rather a tumult was made, he took water, and washed his hands before the multitude, saying, I am innocent of the blood of this just person: see ye to it. Then answered all the people, and said, His blood be on us, and on our children.

Then released he Barabbas unto them: and when he had scourged Jesus, he delivered Him to be crucified.

Then the soldiers of the governor took Jesus into the common hall, and gathered unto Him the whole band of soldiers. And they stripped Him, and put on Him a scarlet robe.

And when they had platted a crown of thorns, they put it upon His head, and a reed in His right hand: and they bowed the knee before Him, and mocked Him, saying, Hail, King of the Jews! And they spit upon Him, and took the reed, and smote Him on the head.

ECCE HOMO *by Philippe de Champaigne (1602–1674). Image from Art Resource/ Réunion des Musées Nationaux, Musées des Granges de Port-Royal, France. Photograph by Hervé Lewandowski.*

Resurrection

Luke 24: 1–11, 13–16, 25–27, 30–31

Now upon the first day of the week, very early in the morning, they came unto the sepulchre, bringing the spices which they had prepared, and certain others with them. And they found the stone rolled away from the sepulchre. And they entered in, and found not the body of the Lord Jesus.

And it came to pass, as they were much perplexed thereabout, behold, two men stood by them in shining garments: And as they were afraid and bowed down their faces to the earth, they said unto them, Why seek ye the living among the dead? He is not here, but is risen: remember how he spake unto you when he was yet in Galilee, Saying, The Son of man must be delivered into the hands of sinful men, and be crucified, and the third day rise again.

And they remembered his words, And returned from the sepulchre and told all these things unto the eleven, and to all the rest. It was Mary Magdalene, and Joanna, and Mary the mother of James, and other women that were with them, which told these things unto the apostles. And their words seemed to them as idle tales, and they believed them not.

And, behold, two of them went that same day to a village called Emmaus, which was from Jerusalem about threescore furlongs. And they talked together of all these things which had happened.

And it came to pass, that, while they communed together and reasoned, Jesus Himself drew near and went with them. But their eyes were holden that they should not know Him.

Then He said unto them, O fools, and slow of heart to believe all that the prophets have spoken: Ought not Christ to have suffered these things and to enter into His glory?

And beginning at Moses and all the prophets, He expounded unto them in all the scriptures the things concerning Himself.

And it came to pass, as He sat at meat with them, He took bread, and blessed it, and brake, and gave to them. And their eyes were opened, and they knew Him; and He vanished out of their sight.

THE SUPPER AT EMMAUS *by Philippe de Champaigne (1602-1674). Image from Art Resource/Réunion des Musées Nationaux, Musée des Beaux-Arts, Nantes, France. Photograph by Gérard Blot.*

That First Easter

Becky Jennings

When the organ music swells
And the church begins to fill,
May we remember Gethsemane
And a cross on Calvary's hill.

When we don our Easter finery
And stroll proudly down the street,
Keep in mind the bleeding nail prints
In His hands and in His feet.

Don't forget the awful suffering
For our sins He had to pay
And His wondrous Resurrection
On that first glad Easter Day.

*John Clayton Adams (1840–1906) portrays
a beautiful spring day in his painting*
Spring Blossom. *Image from Fine Art
Photographic LIbrary, Ltd., London/
N. R. Omell Gallery, London.*

O my Savior, make me see how dearly Thou has paid for me, That lost

The Light of Easter

Erma Stull Grove

Lord God of Hosts, we give Thee thanks
For the light of an Easter dawn,
When joy breaks through in life anew
And the fears of the night are gone.
Like Mary Magdalene may we
Seek His presence and hear His voice;
With hope imbued, with strength renewed,
We can sing, "He is risen! Rejoice!"

Lord God of Hosts, we give Thee thanks
For the light of an Easter morn,
When clouds of doubt are put to rest
And a radiant faith's reborn.
Like Peter and like John may we
Seek His face, understand His choice;
With reverent hearts our courage starts,
And we sing, "He is risen! Rejoice!"

Lord God of Hosts, we give Thee thanks
For the light of an Easter day,
When love can win, over wrong and sin,
A victory that lights our way.
Like Emmaus travelers may we
In the breaking of bread rejoice;
No mystery eternity,
When we sing, "He is risen! Rejoice!"

Lord God of Hosts, we give Thee thanks
For the light of an Easter night;
Gone doubt and fears, sorrow and tears—
In their place an endless delight.
Like those of old whose lives were changed
By the peace from Thy gentle voice,
Triumphantly we rise with Thee,
Ever singing in praise, "Rejoice!"

again my life may prove as then in death so now in love. —Richard Crashaw

He Lives Again

Harry E. Ezell

Though fear had turned the crowd away
Who once had strewed flowers in His path,
Though Judas by a kiss betrayed
Our Lord to mockery and death,
The singing bells of Easter time
Ring out the glorious refrain
And heavenward raise the song sublime,
"Our Lord is risen, He lives again."

Though Pilate in a silver bowl
Would wash away his guilty stain,
The unjust sentence weighed his soul;
The sentence he had passed in vain,
For singing bells of Easter time
Ring out the glorious refrain
And heavenward raise the song sublime,
"Our Lord is risen, He lives again."

Though Calvary's bloodstained earth has borne
The Cross on which our Savior died,
Though His poor body, bruised and torn,
Within the grave was laid aside,
Still, singing bells of Easter time
Ring out the glorious refrain
And heavenward raise the song sublime,
"Our Lord is risen, He lives again."

Then let the shining stars above,
Let all the lowly race of men
In paeans of gratitude and love
Join in the song as, once again,
Glad singing bells of Easter time
Ring out the glorious refrain
And heavenward raise the song sublime,
"Our Lord is risen, He lives again."

The sun sets over sand verbena and dune primrose in Anza-Borrego Desert State Park, California. Photograph by Christopher Talbot Frank.

Easter Music

Judy Lea

THE SOLO

Solo means alone, but you were not. It was your voice, your golden throat and that mighty bellows of muscle in your chest that produced the notes.

But where did the Spirit come from?

It came from all of us around you who breathed as you breathed and prayed as you prayed for that overpowering, heart-bursting sound that again brought indescribable pleasures to our hearing ears and God's blessings to our hungry souls.

THE DUET

His voice is polished, shining, and rich like walnut. It is smooth and warm, heated by an internal energy that breathes it into life. It curves throughout the center and has tapered edges like a circular banister, solid, strong, and supportive, yet creating a sense of textured beauty that reflects the sensitive and the tender.

Her voice is like a square of royal purple velvet. It glides from a taughtly pulled diamond with distinctly rolled edges into a rectangle that releases itself drifting gently to drape over and around, but never through, the sculpted bar. The loose hems fall over and down to enfold and absorb steps in the octave but never the whole, yet share a sense of the message and the mission.

THE TRIO

How can the pitches high, medium, and low be fused to become one energy, one power, one sound?

An artist would know, as he mixes these tints to make a perfect hue.

A mother would know, as she braids the silky hair of a precious daughter.

A man and a woman and child would know, as they bond together in family love.

And God knows—the Father, Son, and Holy Spirit—as he takes three separate and distinct voices and blends them together in a hymn that is sung from the foot of the Cross.

Wildflowers on Long Ridge above Imnaha River Canyon, Oregon, grace the hillsides. Photograph by Terry Donnelly/Donnelly Austin Photography.

Monday Morning Afterglow

Dorothy Taggart

Deceptive is this silence in the sanctuary,
Where lingers still the faint perfume of flowers
And of those who came to worship in thanksgiving,
Or the heavy-hearted, peace and comfort seeking,
In quiet, labored thoughts at once reflective
Of disobedience and of old transgressions,
Their universal prayers petitioned,
And their voices raised in praise and adoration
For the promise that is given to the righteous
In Holy Words of reconciliation,
Spoken beneath the naked Cross, magnetic,
And offered in the choral benediction:
"Angels descending, bring from above
Echoes of mercy, whispers of love."

Yet Listen Now

Amy Carmichael

Yet listen now,
Oh, listen with the wondering olive trees,
And the white moon that looked between the leaves,
And gentle earth that shuddered as she felt
Great drops of blood. All torturing questions find
Answer beneath those old grey olive trees.
There, only there, we can take heart to hope
For all lost lambs—aye, even for ravening wolves.
Oh, there are things done in the world today
Would root up faith, but for Gethsemane.

For Calvary interprets human life;
No path of pain but there we meet our Lord;
And all the strain, the terror, and the strife
Die down like waves before His peaceful word,
And nowhere but beside the awful Cross,
And where the olives grow along the hill,
Can we accept the unexplained, the loss,
The crushing agony, and hold us still.

The interior of the Round Church in Richmond, Vermont, is bright on a spring morning. Photograph by William H. Johnson.

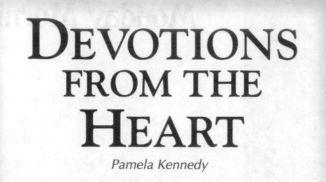

Devotions from the Heart

Pamela Kennedy

As they were going out, they met a man from Cyrene, named Simon, and they forced him to carry the cross. — Matthew 27:32

Compelled to be Kind

A few years ago our church started a program called Helping Hands. It was a "talent bank" from which help could be withdrawn when someone in the church had a special need. I signed up and felt good about participating in a practical program of Christian charity.

A year went by before I was called by the Helping Hands chairman.

"Miss Alice was in a car accident several weeks ago," he said. "She broke both her legs and has been in the hospital and then in rehab. Now she's back in her apartment. We'd like to provide her meals for the next few weeks. You signed up volunteering to help. Could you bring Miss Alice dinners tomorrow, Thursday, and Saturday?"

I looked at the stack of papers I had to correct and my empty cupboards. We had guests coming in a few days, and I wasn't ready. I wanted to say "No, I can't," but I felt compelled. "Okay, sure," I said, with as much enthusiasm as I could muster. I called Miss Alice to ask what she enjoyed. "Oh, just anything dear. You're so kind."

I rushed to the store to pick up groceries for our incoming guests. I selected some nice salmon steaks, some asparagus from the produce department, and a single serving of cheesecake in the bakery. On the way out, I grabbed fresh flowers to put in the guest bedroom.

The next day, I dashed home from work, quickly broiled the salmon and steamed the asparagus. I tossed a salad and tucked a couple of whole-wheat rolls into a napkin. Carefully placing everything into a basket, I plucked a few of the flowers from my arrangement and put them in

---

Dear Lord, I thank You for the opportunity to help others whenever the need arises. May I be a gracious giver each time I'm asked to serve.

---

a bud vase. Heading out the door, I remembered a little devotional book I had recently purchased. I slipped it into the basket. I was feeling rushed and anxious, not overcome by Christian charity.

When I knocked on the apartment door, Miss Alice called out, "Come in, please!" At first, I couldn't even see her. The apartment was dim, and she was sitting on the couch enveloped in pillows. The small room was cluttered with papers and furniture, and it was obvious no one had been

This array of flowers and baskets would cheer anyone, even on a rainy spring day. Photograph by Nancy Matthews.

by recently to tidy things up. But Miss Alice was beaming.

"I can't tell you how much these meals mean to me," she said. Her eyes watered with unshed tears. "I am so lonely. I used to walk three miles every day. I haven't been outside in two months."

I felt a stab of guilt. "I've brought you some salmon and asparagus. And there's a piece of cheesecake for dessert." I arranged the food on her little table and helped her get to the chair. Then I placed the bud vase in the center of the table and set the book next to it.

"Oh, would you read to me?" she asked, her eyes hopeful as a child's.

"Of course." I sat at the table and read as she ate, my anxiety and frustration dissolving.

On the way home, I whispered a prayer of thanks. Miss Alice had told me about her family, her trouble with healing, and her discouragement.

Then she said, "But God is answering my prayers through people like you, and I know He'll work out all things well."

I had reluctantly gone to offer a hand, never realizing that I was the one in need of help—help remembering that it is in serving we are blessed.

When I read again the account of Christ's passion, my attention is drawn to the character of Simon. Here was a man from Africa on a Passover pilgrimage to Jerusalem. Then, right in the middle of his mission, he is compelled to carry the cross of Christ the last several yards to Golgotha. I can only imagine how that act must have affected Simon. He offered Jesus the last act of kindness he experienced on this earth. What an incredible blessing! Acts of charity are easy when we feel like doing them, but sometimes the greatest joy comes when we are compelled to be kind.

The Eternal Goodness

John Greenleaf Whittier

I know not what the future hath
Of marvel or surprise,
Assured alone that life and death
His mercy underlies.

And if my heart and flesh are weak
To bear an untried pain,
The bruised reed He will not break,
But strengthen and sustain.

No offering of my own I have,
Nor works my faith to prove;
I can but give the gifts He gave,
And plead His love for love.

And so beside the Silent Sea
I wait the muffled oar;
No harm from Him can come to me
On ocean or on shore.

I know not where His islands lift
Their fronded palms in air;
I only know I cannot drift
Beyond His love and care.

The clear, golden light of a spring day highlights the beauty of the forest in this painting, entitled A FOREST GLADE, by Johannes Boesen (1847–1916). Image from Fine Art Photographic Library, Ltd., London/Private Collection.

Barter

Sara Teasdale

Life has loveliness to sell,
    All beautiful and splendid things,
Blue waves whitened on a cliff,
    Soaring fire that sways and sings,
And children's faces looking up
Holding wonder like a cup.

Life has loveliness to sell,
    Music like a curve of gold,
Scent of pine trees in the rain,
    Eyes that love you, arms that hold,
And, for your spirit's still delight,
Holy thoughts that star the night.

Spend all you have for loveliness,
    Buy it and never count the cost;
For one white singing hour of peace
    Count many a year of strife well lost,
And for a breath of ecstasy
Give all you have been, or could be.

*Lupine and balsamroot decorate the
Columbia River Gorge National Scenic Area.
Photograph by Steve Terrill.*

SOMEONE TO REMEMBER

Michelle Prater Burke

A GRANDMOTHER'S GIFT

For almost twenty years now, I have worn around my wrist three thin gold bracelets. They have become so much a part of me that I sometimes forget they are there, except when my children say they can hear me "jingle" as the bangles jostle together. The bracelets were given to me by my maternal grandmother, who brought them from Iran during her first visit to America. The bracelets were wrapped inside a pink drawstring bag adorned with her embroidery work, but they were much too large for my six-year-old wrist. I could push them up my entire arm. But Grandmama had faith I would grow into her gift, and I was told to think of her whenever I looked at them.

I visited with Grandmama only a few more times in my life. She spoke very limited English, yet I never felt alienated by our language barrier. Instead I was fascinated by our differences and drawn closer to her by the few words she did know, such as "come" and "eat." By then, she was an aging grandmother with wise eyes and wispy gray hair pulled back at her nape. But my mother has told me the remarkable tales of an earlier time in Grandmama's life, a time when she was a dedicated young mother raising a growing family in Iran.

Born around 1906, Nanajon Golpashin was of Assyrian and Armenian descent. Along with my grandfather, Isaac, she raised eight children in Iran during the Shah Mohammed Reza Pahlavi's reign, when Western culture was prevalent and communities were filled with Protestants, Catholics, and Muslims living side by side. I am told that Grandmama was a woman who expected everyone to work hard and that she had unwavering convictions. When the local Presbyterian church rang its bells for worship or Bible classes, she made sure her children were there; and when beggars stood at her door, she kindly offered household jobs and packed food and clothing for them when they left.

Unlike many women of her day, Grandmama was educated; and her degree in home economics allowed her to skillfully handle the needs of her large family. She taught needlework to the girls

---

Perhaps it is the tender tales of my grandmother's life that I enjoy the most.

---

and diligently checked all chores and homework before bedtime. She spoke Armenian, Assyrian, Turkish, and Farsi and taught her children these languages, in addition to the English lessons they had at school. Perhaps it was her own schooling that led Grandmama to encourage all her children, daughters included, to become educated in an era when higher education was not the norm. Her children went on to schools in America, Turkey, Canada, India, Germany, and Iran. My mother tells me that at times the children fretted over how the family could afford tuition for all of them, but Grandmama would assure them not to

worry. "You just study and pray," she would say, "and Papa and I will take care of the rest."

Perhaps it is the tender tales of my grandmother's life that I enjoy the most. Some stories tell of the summers she shared with the children at the family's vineyard in the country. Another personal favorite of mine took place one Christmas Eve when her older children had been disputing the existence of Santa Claus in front of their younger siblings. Grandmama quietly climbed onto the flat roof and threw several balls down the chimney, to the surprise of the doubting children below.

But beyond the demands of family life, Grandmama faced fears and disappointments I have never known. During a time of political unrest in the 1940s, she and her children hid in a pomegranate truck and fled to Tehran in the middle of the night to reunite with my grandfather, who had been smuggled to the city six months earlier. The political climate would affect my grandmother's life again many years later. When she and Grandpapa left their homeland and immigrated to the United States, she had to leave behind a beloved country in turmoil and a culture that was fading. It was this culture and her experiences within it that shaped her as the matriarch she became and, in turn, shaped the generations that would follow her.

As I try to cultivate character in my own children, I sometimes think of Grandmama. Although she raised her family in a time and an environment that no longer exist, her hopes and dreams for them were much like mine; and her eight children would not forget her example of respect for knowledge and generosity, courage and faith. May I hope to do as well.

I never remove the gold bracelets that rest on my wrist, for they keep my grandmother's legacy close and her memory real. One day, I hope to pass them on to my own daughter and tell her the story of a strong, Assyrian woman named Nana and the three bracelets that link our lives.

Michelle Prater Burke is a former editor of IDEALS. *She lives with her husband and their three children in Middle Tennessee.*

Original art by Susan Harrison.

Beauty

Frank H. Keith

Would you be beautiful, truly so?
The way is not mystic or new.
Drink something of beauty
    from all that you see,
And it will live on in you.

This Day of Days

Gail Brook Burket

The leaves a day ago too small,
Tomorrow fully grown,
Now hold enchantment in their thrall
For these fleet hours alone.
And on this gleaming day of days,
When half-grown leaves design
With dappled sun a patterned maze,
Half playful, half divine,
I treasure all things beautiful,
Hope memory may bring
Me glimpses of this miracle
Until another spring.

Lovely Things

Edith Shaw Butler

Treasure all such lovely things:
A sudden flash of bright blue wings
On days when field and hill are bright,
A starry, frost-clear April night,
The misty green of trees in spring,
The tinkling song the peepers sing,
The flaming colors of the dawn,
A rainbow arching distant hills,
Early garden daffodils,
Meadows trimmed with Queen Anne laces,
Fragrant ferns in woodland places,
A season-painted countryside,
A home where peace and love abide.
He holds the wealth that beauty brings
Who cherishes such lovely things.

A cascade of fuchsia-colored blossoms on a rhododendron in Washington Park Arboretum in Seattle, Washington, is a beautiful example of spring pleasures for the eyes. Photograph by Mary Liz Austin/Donnelly Austin Photography.

Woodnotes

Ralph Waldo Emerson

When the pine tosses its cones
To the song of its waterfall tones,
Who speeds to the woodland walks?
To birds and trees, who talks?
Caesar of his leafy Rome,
There the poet is at home.
He goes to the river-side,
Not hook nor line hath he;
He stands in the meadows wide,
Nor gun nor scythe to see.
In the wood he travels glad,
Without better fortune had,
Melancholy without bad.
Knowledge this man prizes best
Seems fantastic to the rest:
Pondering shadows, colors, clouds,
Grass-buds and caterpillar-shrouds,
Boughs on which the wild bees settle,
Tints that spot the violet's petal,
Why Nature loves the number five,
And why the star-form she repeats:
Lover of all things alive,
Wonderer at all he meets,
Wonderer chiefly at himself,
Who can tell him what he is?

*Now, on a sudden, I know it,
the secret, the secret
of life. . . . 'Tis unrolled as
a scroll to all eyes in the
curve of the waterfall.*

—HARRY LYMAN KOOPMAN

*In Mount Hood National Forest, a wild rhododendron's blossoms
provide a delicate accompaniment to the graceful movement of
a creek. Photograph by Steve Terrill.*

FOR THE CHILDREN

My Heart Knows

Eileen Spinelli

Do you know it's spring, wide sky?
Of course, you do—
    you're springtime blue.
Do you know it's spring, little bird?
And is that why
    you sing flying by?
Do you know it's spring, yellow bee,
    and time to make more honey?
Do you know it's spring, tulip and bunny,
    cherry tree, willow, and geese on the wing?
I know it's spring!

My coat's tucked away;
The garden is planted;
There's more time to play
    with my friends in the park
    on seesaw and swing.
My heart feels so happy;
    my heart knows it's spring.

A young girl gives special care to her furry friend in this painting, entitled Some Bunny to Love, *by Kathryn Andrews Fincher.*

Endymion: Book 1

John Keats

A thing of beauty is a joy for ever:
Its loveliness increases; it will never
Pass into nothingness; but still will keep
A bower quiet for us, and a sleep
Full of sweet dreams, and health,
     and quiet breathing.
Therefore, on every morrow, are we wreathing
A flowery band to bind us to the earth,
Spite of despondence, of the inhuman dearth
Of noble natures, of the gloomy days,
Of all the unhealthy and o'er-darkened ways
Made for our searching: yes, in spite of all,
Some shape of beauty moves away the pall
From our dark spirits. Such the sun, the moon,
Trees old, and young, sprouting a shady boon
For simple sheep; and such are daffodils
With the green world they live in; and clear rills
That for themselves a cooling covert make
'Gainst the hot season; the mid-forest brake,
Rich with a sprinkling of fair musk-rose blooms.

Everyday Beauty

Hazel Spaulding Franks

I have seen the best upon this earth
    Though I have not traveled far;
I have peeped into a bluebird's nest
    And traced a falling star.

I have seen the might of thunderstorms,
    The fragility of a tear,
The timelessness of mountain heights,
    The fleetness of a year.

I have known the changing seasons,
    The raindrops' silver shower,
The sharing of a whispered word,
    The setting sun's brief hour.

These things I have seen are everyday—
    We have but to use our eyes
To find the beauty of God's world
    As boundless as His skies.

Spring tulips in Skagit Valley, Washington, are a vibrant burst of color for the warmer days of spring. Photograph by Jon Gnass.

FAMILY RECIPES

Easter holidays are a special time for family and friends to gather around a table filled with foods lovingly prepared. We hope you enjoy these selections from IDEALS readers. We would love to try your favorite recipe too. Send a typed copy to IDEALS Publications, 535 Metroplex Drive, Suite 250, Nashville, Tennessee 37211. Payment will be provided for each recipe published.

CHICKEN LYNN
Sharon Jarden, Westin, West Virginia

4 chicken breasts, cubed
1 10 3/4-ounce can cream of
   chicken soup
1 8-ounce carton sour cream

1/3 cup chicken broth
1 stack butter crackers, crushed
4 tablespoons melted butter

Preheat oven to 350°F. Arrange chicken cubes in a 9- x 12-inch buttered baking dish. In a large bowl, combine soup, sour cream, and broth; whisk until mixed thoroughly. Pour sauce over chicken. Pour melted butter over cracker crumbs and mix thoroughly; sprinkle over top of casserole. Bake 20 minutes or until casserole begins to bubble. Makes 8 servings.

EXTRA SPECIAL CHICKEN
Mable Long, Columbia, Kentucky

4 chicken breasts
3 tablespoons butter
1/2 cup chopped onion
1/2 cup chopped green pepper

1 cup canned tomatoes
1 cup chicken broth
1 cup beef consommé
1 clove garlic, crushed

Preheat oven to 350°F. Brown chicken in butter; season with salt and pepper. Remove to 9- x 12-inch baking dish. In a large bowl, combine onion, green pepper, tomatoes, chicken broth, beef consommé, and garlic. Mix thoroughly and pour over chicken. Bake 1 hour or until chicken is tender. Makes 4 servings.

Rosemary

Sage

Thyme

Chives

CHICKEN BUNDLES

Naomi Dyer, Eaton, Colorado

2 3-ounce packages cream cheese
    and chives, softened
10 tablespoons melted butter,
    divided
2 cups chopped, cooked chicken

2/3 cup canned mushrooms
2/3 cup crushed herb stuffing
1/3 cup pecans, chopped
2 cans refrigerated crescent rolls
    (16 rolls)

Preheat oven to 375°F. In a large bowl, combine cream cheese with 4 tablespoons of melted butter; mix well. Stir in chicken and mushrooms; set aside. In a small bowl, mix together stuffing and nuts; set aside. Separate dough into 16 triangles. Spread each with 1/4 cup chicken mixture. Roll up into crescent; press edges to seal. Dip in remaining melted butter; roll in stuffing mixture. Place on ugreased cookie sheet; do not allow sides to touch. Bake 15 minutes, or until golden. Makes 8 servings.

CHICKEN AND ASPARAGUS CASSEROLE

Margaret Anderson, Dunkerton, Iowa

1 8-ounce package fine noodles
1 10 3/4-ounce can cream of
    chicken soup
1 10 3/4-ounce can mushroom soup
1/2 cup mayonnaise
1 cup canned mushrooms
    with juice

2 cups chopped, cooked chicken
1 15-ounce can asparagus tips,
    drained
1/2 cup grated Cheddar cheese,
    divided
1 green pepper, diced
1/2 cup chopped almonds

Preheat oven to 350°F. Cook noodles according to package directions; drain and set aside. In a large bowl, combine soups, mayonnaise, green pepper, and mushrooms; mix well. Stir in chicken. In a 9- x 13-inch baking dish, layer half of noodles, asparagus, cheese, and chicken mixture; add half of green pepper and almonds. Repeat layers. Cover and bake 45 minutes or until bubbly. Makes 10 servings.

READERS' FORUM

Right: What happened to those chocolate eggs? Nine-month-old Samuel Craig Huffaker, son of Matt and Rebecca Huffaker of Whittier, California, is a nice Easter surprise for his family.

Left: Samuel Voncannon, three years old, enjoys being outside and paused just long enough for this picture taken by his grandmother, Geneva Voncannon, of Seagrove, North Carolina.

Below: Eighteen-month-old Alexandria Elizabeth Evans gently touches an early daffodil. She is the daughter of Craig and Catherine Evans of Columbia, Illinois, and the great-granddaughter of Dorothy Hoffman, also of Columbia.

Left: A perfect red tulip, although beautiful, is not as pretty as three-year-old Alysa Duke, dressed in the lovely lavender of spring. Alysa is the daughter of Esther Duke and the granddaughter of Roger and Charlotte Duke of Monroe, Georgia.

Right: Twenty-month-old Lili Cae Dase is content to rest gracefully at the home of her great-grandparents, Lyle and Ronda Krogman, in rural Celina, Ohio. She is the daughter of Matt and Carrie Dase of Granville, Ohio.

Below: Ready for the Easter parade, Abby Lilly, age four, daughter of Ronald and Sandra Lilly and granddaughter of Gloria Terlouw, poses with spring daffodils. The family lives in Havre de Grace, Maryland.

THANKS TO ALL who shared family photographs with IDEALS for this issue. If you would like to send snapshots to share with the IDEALS family, please send only duplicates and include a self-addressed, stamped envelope. List your name, address, and telephone number. We are also interested in appealing pet photographs for the Friendship issue. Please mail to:

Readers' Forum
Ideals Publications
535 Metroplex Drive, Suite 250
Nashville, Tennessee 37211

Dear Reader,

Spring is the favorite season of most poets. With the reaffirmation of new life and growth all around us—in the warming of the earth, the flowering of our gardens, and the beautiful coloring of the countryside—each of us can see, again, in ourselves and the conduct of our lives wonderful possibilities. And we should remember to thank the poets for reminding us of this.

With the first issue for 2005, we have introduced some new features. For *Hometown America*, I invite all our readers who grew up in a town of a population of ten thousand or less to write an essay describing what it was like. For *Someone to Remember*, write about someone special in your past. Submissions should be limited to 700 words for each feature with your name and address on each page. Mail them to *Ideals*, 535 Metroplex Drive, Suite 250, Nashville, Tennessee, 37211. These will not be returned.

We at *Ideals* wish the loveliest spring season to our friends and readers.

Marjorie L. Lloyd

ideals®

Publisher, Patricia A. Pingry
Editor, Marjorie Lloyd
Designer, Marisa Calvin
Copy Editor, Marie Brown
Permissions Editor, Patsy Jay
Contributing Writers, Kelly Riley Baugh, Michelle Prater Burke, Lansing Christman, Joan Donaldson, Pamela Kennedy, and Elizabeth Raum

ACKNOWLEDGMENTS

CAMPBELL, ANNE. "The Seed Catalog Arrives." Originally appeared in *Home and Holiday Verse*, selected by Louella Everett, published by Blue Ribbon Books, Inc., 1939. Our sincere thanks to the author's Estate. CARMICHAEL, AMY "Yet Listen Now" from *Mountain Breezes* by Amy Carmichael, Copyright © by the Dohnavur Fellowship, published by CLC Publications, Fort Washington, PA. Used by permission. JAQUES, EDNA. "April" from *Beside Still Waters*. Copyright © 1939 by Thomas Allen Ltd. Rights returned to Edna Jaques. Used by permission of Louise Bonnell. Our sincere thanks to those authors, or their heirs, some of whom we were unable to locate, who submitted poems or articles to *Ideals* for publication. Every possible effort has been made to acknowledge ownership of material used.

Inside back cover: What is spring without gentle breezes and high-flying kites? This painting, by John Morgan (1823–1886), is entitled, appropriately, THE KITE. Image from Fine Art Photographic Library, Ltd, London/Waterhouse & Dodd.

STATEMENT OF OWNERSHIP, MANAGEMENT AND CIRCULATION (REQUIRED BY FORM 3526)

1. Publication Title: Ideals. 2. Publication Number: 0019-137X. 3. Filing Date: August 12, 2004. 4. Issue Frequency: 6. 5. Number of Issues Published Annually: 6. 6. Annual Subscription Price: $19.95. 7. Office of publication: Guideposts, A Church Corporation, 39 Seminary Hill Road, Carmel, NY 10512. 8. Location of headquarters: Guideposts, A Church Corporation, 39 Seminary Hill Road, Carmel, NY 10512. 9. The names and addresses of the publisher and the editor-in-chief are: Patricia A. Pingry, Ideals Publications, A Division of Guideposts, 535 Metroplex Dr., Ste. 250, Nashville, TN 37211; Editor: Marjorie L. Lloyd (same as publisher); Managing Editor: Marjorie L. Lloyd (same as publisher). 10. Owner: Guideposts, A Church Corporation, a New York not for-profit corporation, 39 Seminary Hill Road, Carmel, NY 10512. Names and addresses of individual owners; None. 11 The known bondholders, mortgagees, and other security holders owning or holding one percent or more of total amount of bonds, mortgages or other securities: None. 12. The exempt status has not changed during preceding 12 months 13. Publication Name: Ideals. 14. Issue Date for Circulation Data: Thanksgiving '03 thru Friendship '04. 15 Average number of copies each issue during preceding twelve months: a. total number of copies printed: 138,726; b. (1) paid and/or requested circulation through outside-county mail subscriptions: 106,033; (2) paid and/or requested circulation through in-county subscriptions: None; (3) paid and/or requested circulation through dealer sales: 8,069; (4) paid and/or requested circulation through other classes: None; c.total paid and/or requested circulation: 114,102. d. (1) free distribution by mail through outside-county: 841; (2) free distribution by mail through in-county: None; (3) free distribution by mail through other classes: None; e. free distribution outside the mail: 1,740; f. total free distribution: 2,581; g. total distribution: 116,683; h. copies not distributed: 22,043; i. total 138,726. Percent Paid and/or requested circulation: 97.8%. Actual number of copies of single issue published nearest to filing date: 15.a. total number of copies printed: 131,027; b. (1) paid and/or requested circulation through outside-county mail subscriptions: 117,121; (2) paid and/or requested circulation through in-county subscriptions: None; (3) paid and/or requested circulation through dealer sales: 3,642; (4) paid and/or requested circulation through other classes: None; c. total paid and/or requested circulation: 120,763; d. (1) free distribution by mail through outside-county: 1,000; (2) free distribution by mail through in-county: None; (3) free distribution by mail through other classes: None; e. free distribution outside the mail: None; f. total free distribution: 1,000; g. total distribution: 121,763; h. copies not distributed: 9,264; i. total: 131,027. Percent Paid and/or requested circulation: 99.2%. 16. This Statement of Ownership will be printed in the Easter '05 issue of this publication. 17. I certify that the statements made to me above are correct and complete. Signed John F. Temple, President.